I DON'T DO
ORDINARY

First published in 2007 by
Ravette Publishing Ltd
Unit 3, Tristar Centre, Star Road,
Partridge Green, West Sussex RH13 8RA

ISBN: 978-1-84161-281-2

I DON'T DO ORDINARY

ℛℛ
RAVETTE PUBLISHING

TOO MUCH FOOD IS NEVER ENOUGH

HEY,
THIS CAT IS ONE
CLASS ACT!

You're only young once,
but you can be
immature forever.

I DON'T DO CONFORMITY!

How can pizza and stretch pants be popular at the same time?

I've got a hundred gigabytes of disk space, and six phone numbers stored on it.

Anything worth doing, is worth overdoing.

IT'S NOT
LOGICAL
IT'S JUST OUR
POLICY

I ALWAYS ACT MY AGE

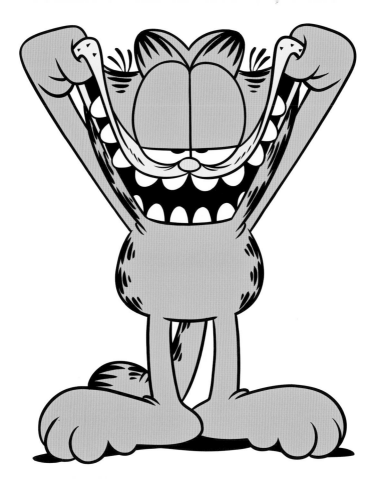

My ball isn't lost,
it's just directionally
challenged.

AN IMPORTANT PART
OF ANY
FITNESS PROGRAMME
IS A
BALANCED BREAKFAST

Older, yes.
Wiser, maybe.
Weirder, definitely!

IF IN DOUBT, ACT STUPID.

Coffee kick-starts my brain

I'M IN A LEAGUE OF MY OWN.

Only wimps ask
for directions
on the information
superhighway!

THE BEST THINGS IN LIFE ARE EDIBLE.

Other GARFIELD Gift Books published by Ravette ...

	ISBN	Price
Gift Books (hardback)		
Don't Know Don't Care	978-1-84161-279-9	£4.99
Get a Grip	978-1-84161-282-9	£4.99
Keep your attitude, I have my own	978-1-84161-278-2	£4.99
Little Books (paperback)		
C-c-c-caffeine	978-1-84161-183-9	£2.50
Food 'n' Fitness	978-1-84161-145-7	£2.50
Laughs	978-1-84161-146-4	£2.50
Love 'n' Stuff	978-1-84161-147-1	£2.50
Surf 'n' Sun	978-1-84161-186-0	£2.50
The Office	978-1-84161-184-6	£2.50
Zzzzzz	978-1-84161-185-3	£2.50

All Garfield books are available at your local bookshop or from the publisher at the address below.

Just send your order with your payment and name and address details to:-
Ravette Publishing, Unit 3, Tristar Centre, Star Road, Partridge Green,
West Sussex RH13 8RA (tel: 01403 711443   email: ravettepub@aol.com)

Prices and availability are subject to change without prior notice.

Please enclose a cheque or postal order made payable to Ravette Publishing
to the value of the cover price of the books and allow the following for UK p&p:-

70p for the first book + 40p for each additional book.